The Birds Who Suffer From the Cold

Published by Treasure Tower Books
The children's book division of the SGI-USA
606 Wilshire Blvd., Santa Monica, CA 90401
© 2007 SGI-USA

ISBN 978-1-932911-31-2

Cover and interior design by SunDried Penguin Design

10 9 8 7 6 5 4 3 2 1

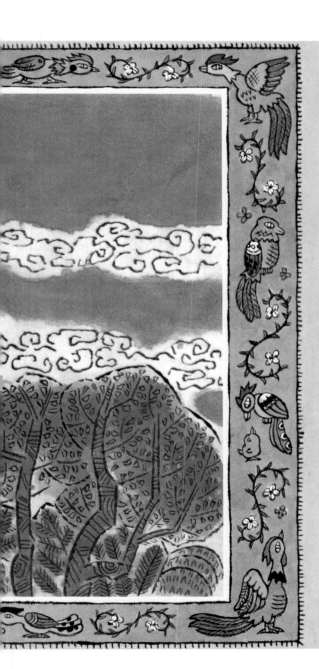

Long ago and far away, in the towering Snow Mountains of India, snow fell all year round. At night, it was terribly, terribly cold.

At the top of these wintry mountains lived a family of little birds who, night after night, suffered in the numbing cold. Every night, their wings iced over, icicles hung off their beaks, and when they cried because they were so cold, their tears froze into little ice cubes.

Every day, however, the birds played in the sunshine and never thought about building a warm nest. Then night would fall and they would nearly freeze.

"It's so c-c-c-cold, I have icicles on my wings," said one.

"This is terrible! Tomorrow we should build a nest," said the other.

"Great idea! Let's do it!"

"Hooray for our nest!"

But when the next day came, they played and forgot all about building their nest.

"We'll do it later," they said. But "later" never came, and with no nest, once again they shivered in the cold all night long.

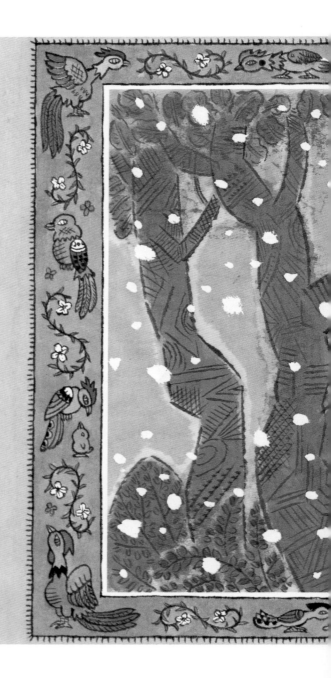

6

As soon as the Sun shone in the Eastern sky, its rays warmed the cold toes and wings and beaks of these birds, and they woke up and began to sing:

> "Hey hey hey,
>
> It's a beautiful day,
>
> It's time to play,
>
> Put cares away.
>
> We've got the Sun,
>
> It's time for fun!
>
> We're feeling great,
>
> That nest can wait!"

They flew from branch to branch, playing tag and hide-the-seed and all sorts of bird games. They never thought once about how cold it would be when night came. They forgot how freezing and miserable they'd been the night before. They played and sang and took little bird-naps and had a wonderful time.

Every morning, all the other birds, who had slept cozily in their warm nests, began to stir. One by one, they flew out, had a little breakfast and went to work on their nests, making sure they'd be warm again when the cold night came.

The two silly birds, however, dashed over to their friends. "Come on," they yelled. "Let's go play! It's a beautiful day! You can do your work later!"

But the other birds didn't listen. They just smiled and waved and kept right on working.

9

"Those other birds are boring! Let's go find some other friends to play with," the silly birds muttered. So they flew off to ask the crickets to come play.

"We'll play after we're done fixing up our den," the busy crickets said.

"How about you ants?" the birds asked. "Do you want to play with us?"

"We're getting our hill ready for tonight," the ants said, "but maybe afterward...."

The two birds went back to their bird friends. "Aw, come on," they begged. "Come play with us. Your boring old nests can wait."

But their bird friends just frowned. "Look," they said, "why don't you go build a nest for yourselves? Night is coming soon. Don't you remember how you cried last night because you were so cold? You're going to be freezing again if you don't build a nest."

The wise old Sun was watching the two birds playing and dancing. "Listen to me, little birds," he called to them. "You should follow your bird friends' advice. And fast! I'm going to leave before too long, and then it will be night. Don't you remember how cold the night is?"

"The Sun is right," said one bird to the other. "We should probably listen to him."

"But we just started a game of tag," said the other silly bird. "And look how pretty the lake is. Don't you want to go swimming?"

"I sure do! Last one in is a rotten egg!"

They just couldn't help themselves; they were having too much fun.

When they finished with their games, they were so tired, they fell asleep. The Sun waved goodbye and disappeared into the western sky. Soon it was dark—too dark to build a nest.

It grew colder and colder. The other birds and animals said goodnight and disappeared into their warm, cozy nests. Soon the only sounds were contented snoring.

But the birds who suffered from the cold were wide awake, shivering and crying.

"It's so c-c-c-cold! I have icicles on my wings!"

"This is terrible! We'd better build a nest tomorrow!"

But as soon as the sun warmed them the next morning, the foolish birds forgot all about building their nest. To this day, they can be heard crying from the cold and promising to build their nests the next day.

23

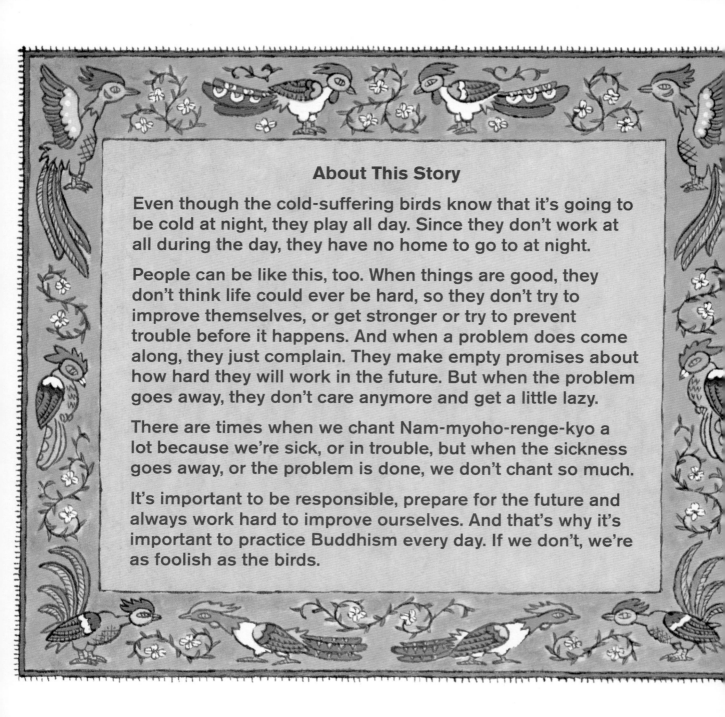

About This Story

Even though the cold-suffering birds know that it's going to be cold at night, they play all day. Since they don't work at all during the day, they have no home to go to at night.

People can be like this, too. When things are good, they don't think life could ever be hard, so they don't try to improve themselves, or get stronger or try to prevent trouble before it happens. And when a problem does come along, they just complain. They make empty promises about how hard they will work in the future. But when the problem goes away, they don't care anymore and get a little lazy.

There are times when we chant Nam-myoho-renge-kyo a lot because we're sick, or in trouble, but when the sickness goes away, or the problem is done, we don't chant so much.

It's important to be responsible, prepare for the future and always work hard to improve ourselves. And that's why it's important to practice Buddhism every day. If we don't, we're as foolish as the birds.